Welcome to Rainbow Bridge Publishing's Mastering Basic Skills "Real-Life" Math Word Problems series. Students often ask their parents and teachers, "When am I ever going to use this?" Mastering Basic Skills—"Real-Life" Math Word Problems has been developed to help students see the many uses of math in the world around them. The word problems in this book help students develop problem-solving skills in real-world situations while increasing confidence in their math skills.

Content for this book is based on current NCTM (National Council of Teachers of Mathematics) standards and supports what teachers are currently using in their classrooms. Word Problems can be used both at school and at home to engage students in problem solving.

The fourth-grade math skills used in this book include addition, subtraction, multiplication, division, graphing, fractions, measurement, area and perimeter, money values and time.

Rainbow Bridge Publishing
www.summerbridgeactivities.com
www.rbpbooks.com

Table of Contents

Name _____ Date _____

◇ Start Here!

Solve each problem. The first problem is worked for you.

1 Anita saw 25 grasshoppers and 16 beetles in the field. How many grasshoppers and beetles did Anita see total?

$$\begin{array}{r} 1 \\ 25 \\ + 16 \\ \hline 41 \end{array}$$ **grasshoppers and beetles**

2 Charley counted 19 more black ants than red ants. Charley counted 34 red ants. How many black ants did Charley count?

3 There were 28 more caterpillars in the flower garden than in the vegetable garden. If there were 31 caterpillars in the vegetable garden, how many caterpillars were there in the flower garden?

4 Eric counted 13 black spiders and 48 brown spiders. How many spiders did Eric count altogether?

5 Jill saw 29 ladybugs in the orchard and 14 ladybugs near the patio. How many ladybugs did Jill see in all?

6 Adam saw 15 bees in the flowers. Later, Adam saw 22 bees in the flowers. How many bees did Adam see altogether?

Bugs are so cool!

7 Marcy saw 21 more butterflies than Jim. Jim saw 19 butterflies. How many butterflies did Marcy see?

Name _____ Date _____

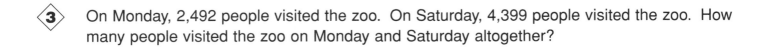

◇ **Start Here!**

Solve each problem. The first problem is worked for you.

1 Jackson fed the penguins 342 pounds of food in March. In May, Jackson fed the penguins 489 pounds of food. How many pounds of food did Jackson feed the penguins total?

$$\begin{array}{r} 342 \\ +\ 489 \\ \hline 831 \end{array}$$ **pounds of food**

2 Laura counted 14 green lizards, 35 snakes and 48 chameleons. How many reptiles did she see in all?

3 On Monday, 2,492 people visited the zoo. On Saturday, 4,399 people visited the zoo. How many people visited the zoo on Monday and Saturday altogether?

4 Alex took 34 pictures of bears, 29 pictures of cats and 48 pictures of reptiles. How many pictures did Alex take altogether?

5 Keshia talks to the zookeeper about what the zoo's birds are fed. The birds ate 3,295 ounces of birdseed in the spring and 2,945 ounces of birdseed in the summer. How many ounces of birdseed did the birds eat in the spring and summer combined?

6 Andy cleaned 45 cages on Monday, 36 cages on Tuesday and 69 cages on Wednesday. How many cages did Andy clean altogether?

7 Lisa walked 72 feet to see the leopards, 129 feet to see the alligators and 218 feet to see the monkeys. How many feet did Lisa walk in all?

8 The zoo has 148 reptiles, 28 mammals and 69 birds. How many animals does the zoo have altogether?

Did you know?
There are 14 reptiles that are on the endangered species list in the U.S. The American crocodile, found in Florida, is among them.

How Tall?

Name _____   Date _____

◇ Start Here!

Solve each problem. The first problem is worked for you.

1 The tallest giant sequoia tree is 275 feet. The tallest coast redwood tree is 321 feet. How much taller is the coast redwood tree than the giant sequoia tree?

$$\begin{array}{r} {\overset{2}{\cancel{3}}}{\overset{1}{\cancel{2}}}1 \\ -\ 275 \\ \hline \textbf{46 feet taller} \end{array}$$

2 The Sears Tower in Chicago is 1,450 feet tall. The John Hancock Center in Chicago is 1,127 feet tall. How much taller is the Sears Tower than the John Hancock Center?

3 The tallest sugar pine tree is 232 feet. The tallest western red cedar tree is 159 feet. How much taller is the sugar pine than the western red cedar?

4 The Empire State Building is 1,250 feet tall. The Chrysler Building is 1,046 feet tall. How much taller is the Empire State Building than the Chrysler Building?

5 Both the Mauna Loa and Kilauea volcanoes are in Hawaii. The Mauna Loa volcano is 13,680 feet tall. The Kilauea volcano is 4,190 feet tall. How much taller is the Mauna Loa volcano than the Kilauea volcano?

6 Mt. Everest, the world's tallest mountain, is 29,035 feet tall. Mt. McKinley is 20,320 feet tall. How much taller is Mt. Everest than Mt. McKinley?

7 The California laurel tree is 108 feet tall. The sitka spruce tree is 191 feet tall. How much taller is the sitka spruce than the California laurel?

Did you know?

The oldest living tree is in California. It is a bristlecone pine tree named Methuselah and is estimated to be 4,700 years old.

Name _____ Date _____

◇ Start Here!

Solve each problem. The first problem is worked for you.

1 Divers saw 432 tropical fish on their first dive, 289 tropical fish on their second dive and 637 tropical fish on their third dive. How many tropical fish did they see altogether?

$$
\begin{array}{r}
432 \\
289 \\
+\,637 \\
\hline
1{,}358 \ \textbf{tropical fish}
\end{array}
$$

2 The Pacific Ocean has an average depth of 12,925 feet. The Gulf of Mexico has an average depth of 5,297 feet. What is the difference in average depth between the Gulf of Mexico and the Pacific Ocean?

3 Misha collected 1,946 seashells. Abe collected 3,479 seashells. How many seashells did Misha and Abe collect in all?

4 A blue whale traveled 1,349 feet the first time it was sighted. The second time it was sighted, the blue whale had traveled another 977 feet. How far did the blue whale travel altogether?

5 A scientist observed 423 sea urchins on his first trip. On his second trip, the scientist observed 296 sea urchins. How many more sea urchins did the scientist observe on his first trip than his second trip?

6 Jason saw 42 octopi, 142 crabs and 339 fish. How many sea creatures did he see altogether?

I see the fish under the sea!

7 Leslie saw 1,228 fewer fish than Taylor. Taylor saw 3,212 fish. How many fish did Leslie see?

8 The dolphin swims 1,268 feet. The shark swims 3,145 feet. How much farther does the shark swim than the dolphin?

Name _____ Date _____

◇Start Here!

Solve each problem. The first problem is worked for you.

1 Hank collects stamps. He buys a rare stamp for $71.93 and a package of stamps for $14.37. How much does Hank spend on stamps?

$$\begin{array}{r} \$71.93 \\ + \$14.37 \\ \hline \$86.30 \end{array}$$

2 At the toy store, Jill spends $95.38 for a doll. Carrie spends $42.69 less than Jill for a doll. How much does Carrie spend?

3 Hector buys a model car for $24.98. Then he spends $18.39 on supplies to build the model car. How much does Hector spend altogether?

4 Mike collects baseball cards. He spends $58.27 on a rookie card. Then he spends $74.93 on his favorite pitcher's card. How much does Mike spend on baseball cards in all?

5 Jack collects aluminum cans for recycling. He earns $23.79 in March and $39.08 in April. How much more money did Jack earn in April than in March?

6 John buys a painting for his collection. He spends $83.67. He gives the clerk $100.00. How much money does he get back?

7 Anne and Jim collect watches. Anne buys a watch for $58.48. Jim pays $39.37 more for his watch. How much does Jim pay?

8 Maria collects stickers. She spends $2.93 at the first store. She spends $12.43 at the second store. How much does Maria spend altogether?

Did you know?
If you had 10 billion $1 bills and spent one every second of every day, it would take 317 years for you to go broke.

Name _____ Date _____

◇Start Here!

Solve each problem using the information in the table.

1 James eats an orange, a peanut butter sandwich and a glass of milk for lunch. How many calories does James eat?

FOOD ITEMS	CALORIES
applesauce	194
celery	9
chicken noodle soup	75
chocolate chip cookies	226
hamburger	369
milk	95
orange	65
peanut butter sandwich	334
pizza (1 slice)	378

```
   65
  334
+  95
 494 calories
```

2 How many more calories does one slice of pizza have than a peanut butter sandwich?

3 If Lisa eats a hamburger and one serving of celery for lunch, how many calories does she eat?

4 What food item in the table has the most calories?

Tuna on rye—my favorite!

5 After school, Amber has chocolate chip cookies and a glass of milk for a snack. How many calories does she eat?

6 For lunch, Daniel orders a bowl of chicken noodle soup, applesauce and chocolate chip cookies. How many calories are in his lunch?

7 What food item in the table has the fewest number of calories?

Name _____   Date _____

◇ Start Here!

Round each number to the nearest ten, hundred or thousand.

Remember...
When you round numbers, look at the number that follows the number you are rounding. For example, when rounding to the nearest ten, if the number you are rounding is followed by 5 or more, you round the number up. If the number you are rounding is followed by 4 or less, you round the number down.

1   In Ashley's school there are 42 students who have computers.
       42 rounded to the nearest 10 = **40**

2   The chess club has 39 members.

3   In Jay's class, 24 students like to go bowling.

Round each number to the nearest hundred.

4   At Rosewood Elementary, there are 369 students who have blue eyes.

5   In the city of Daviston, there are 720 teachers.

6   In Marc's school, 412 students have pets.

Round each number to the nearest thousand.

7   Newton County has a population of 4,700.

8   Randy's school has 2,230 people with blonde hair.

Did you know?
According to the official census, the U.S. population in 2000 was 281,421,906. California is the state with the largest population.

Name _____   Date _____

◇Start Here!

Solve each problem. The first problem is worked for you.

1 Jessica uses 16 ounces of sugar in her lemonade recipe. If she makes 9 batches, how much sugar does she need?

$$\begin{array}{r} \overset{5}{16} \\ \times\,9 \\ \hline 144 \ \ \text{ounces} \end{array}$$

2 Mario sells 324 glasses of lemonade for 3¢ each. How much money does Mario earn?

3 Jamie sells 21 glasses of lemonade every day. If she sells lemonade for a week, how many glasses will she sell?

4 Tracy has 245 gallons of lemonade. She divides the lemonade into 5-gallon pitchers. How many pitchers can she fill?

5 Samantha buys 27 lemons for 9¢ each. How much money does Samantha spend?

6 Norman has 35 ounces of lemonade. He pours it into 5-ounce cups. How many cups of lemonade does he have?

7 Tyler spends 7¢ each for paper cups. If he buys 1,394 cups, how much money does he spend?

8 Kim sells lemonade for a week. Each day she earns $23.49. How much does she earn for the entire week?

9 Jasmine has 128 ounces of lemonade. She divides it equally into 8-ounce glasses. How many glasses of lemonade does Jasmine have?

Name _____   Date _____

◇**Start Here!**

Solve each problem. The first problem is worked for you.

Remember…
- The <u>range</u> is the difference between the highest number and the lowest number in the data.

- To calculate the <u>mean</u> (or average) add the list of numbers and then divide by the number of items.

- The <u>median</u> is the middle number that appears in the data.

- The <u>mode</u> is the number that appears most often in the data.

The Panthers kept track of their scores from their last seven basketball games. Here are their scores:

93,   90,   85,   85,   81,   71,   69

1 What is the range of the basketball scores?

2 What is the mode of the basketball scores?

3 What is the median of the basketball scores?

4 What is the mean of the basketball scores?

Did you know?
Michael Jordan was the NBA scoring leader for ten seasons. In 1987, Michael Jordan earned an average of 37.1 points per game.

Name _____ Date _____

◇ Start Here!

Use the line graph to answer the questions.

1 How many gallons of ice cream were sold in January?

2 gallons

2 Which month had the highest sales?

3 In which month were 4 gallons sold?

4 Which month had the lowest sales?

5 What was the total number of gallons of ice cream sold in February and March?

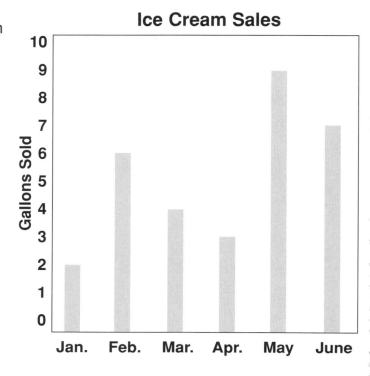

Elizabeth's class voted on their favorite flavors of ice cream. Use the circle graph to answer the questions below.

1 Which flavor of ice cream received the highest number of votes?

2 What percentage of students voted for strawberry ice cream as their favorite flavor?

3 Which flavor of ice cream did 10 percent of the students vote for as their favorite?

4 What was the total percentage of students that liked either chocolate or strawberry best?

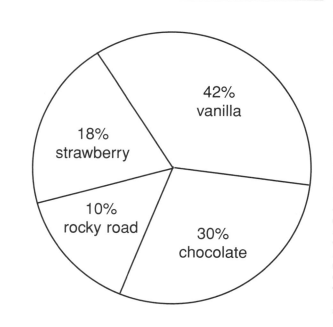

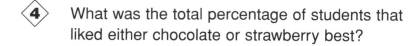

Name _____ Date _____

◇ Start Here!

Solve each problem. The first problem is worked for you.

1 The Sports-R-Us store sells 2 types of tennis rackets. They have 58 of each type of tennis racket. How many tennis rackets does the store have altogether?

$$58$$
$$\times\ 2$$
116 tennis rackets

2 Jack saw 4 times as many footballs as soccer balls in the store. Jack saw 34 soccer balls. How many footballs did Jack see?

3 In the winter season, the Sports-R-Us store sells 5 times as many snowboards as it does during the summer season. The store sells 32 snowboards in the summer season. How many snowboards does the store sell in the winter season?

4 For each display, Tiffany put out 13 dumbbells. If there were 8 different displays, how many dumbbells did Tiffany put out?

5 Steven is checking his inventory. In the spring, he has 3 times as many pairs of skates as in the winter. If Steven has 56 pairs of skates in the winter, how many pairs of skates does he have in the spring?

6 The Sports-R-Us store sold 8 times as many skateboards in June as it sold in September. The store sold 57 skateboards in September. How many skateboards did the store sell in June?

7 Julia sold 6 times as many bicycle helmets as bicycles. Julie sold 18 bicycles. How many bicycle helmets did Julia sell?

8 Coach LaVerde bought 3 times as many baseballs as footballs. If Coach LaVerde bought 28 footballs, how many baseballs did he buy?

Name _____ Date _____

◇Start Here!

Solve each problem. The first problem is worked for you.

1 Casey sells 1,439 magazines every month. How many magazines does Casey sell in 9 months?

$$
\begin{array}{r}
1{,}439 \\
\times\ 9 \\
\hline
12{,}951 \ \text{magazines}
\end{array}
$$

2 Kyle is a reporter for a magazine. He writes 5 articles that each have 598 words. How many words does Kyle write altogether?

3 Webster is a photographer for a magazine. The magazine uses 2 of his pictures on each page. If there are 139 pages in the magazine, how many pictures will Webster need to give them?

4 The Magazine Shop sold 8 times as many magazines as Montgomery's Bookstore. If Montgomery's Bookstore sold 2,587 magazines, how many magazines did the Magazine Shop sell?

5 Monica stocks shelves in the magazine store and puts 7 magazines in each box. Monica has 342 full boxes. How many magazines does Monica have?

6 Ed is a magazine editor. He edits 4 pages each day. How many pages will he edit in 259 days?

7 Diane sells magazine subscriptions. She sells 3,842 subscriptions in one month. How many magazine subscriptions does she sell in 9 months?

Did you know?
Reader's Digest was the top-selling magazine in the U.S. in the year 2000. The magazine's circulation was 12,566,047. The second most popular magazine was *TV Guide*.

Name _____ Date _____

◇ Start Here!

Solve each problem. The first problem is worked for you.

1 Alex buys 7 chocolate chip cookies for $1.24. How much does Alex spend on cookies?

$$\begin{array}{r} \$1.24 \\ \times\ 7 \\ \hline \$8.68 \end{array}$$

2 Jennifer works in a bakery. She earns $5.85 an hour. If Jennifer works 8 hours a day, how much does she earn in one day?

3 Luiz buys 9 cakes for $16.48 each. How much money does Luiz spend?

4 Shelly spends 6 times as much on pies for her party as Tom does. Tom spends $24.83. How much does Shelly spend on pies?

5 Madison, Gary and Annie each buy one dozen doughnuts. One dozen doughnuts costs $7.59. How much do they spend on doughnuts altogether?

6 The bakery earns 7 times as much money selling bagels as it does selling cookies. If the bakery earns $58.39 selling cookies, how much money does the bakery earn selling bagels?

7 Roberto buys 4 boxes of éclairs for his party. Each box of éclairs costs $13.77. How much money does Roberto spend on éclairs?

8 Charlotte spends 7 times more money on peanut butter cookies than John. John spends $23.98 on peanut butter cookies. How much does Charlotte spend?

Did you know?
During the Civil War, the Bureau of Engraving and Printing printed paper money in denominations of 3 cents, 5 cents, 10 cents, 25 cents and 50 cents. Paper money was printed when people hoarded coins, which created a drastic coin shortage.

Name _____ Date _____

◇ Start Here!

Solve each problem. The first problem is worked for you.

1 The California candidate got 34 times more votes than the Florida candidate. The Florida candidate got 85 votes. How many votes did the California candidate get?

$$\begin{array}{r} 85 \\ \times\ 34 \\ \hline 2{,}890 \ \ \textbf{votes} \end{array}$$

2 Twenty-seven students voted for Arthur. Thirty-one times more students voted for Webster. How many students voted for Webster?

3 Amy polled her class to see what the class's favorite kind of pizza was. Thirteen times more students voted for pepperoni pizza than cheese pizza. Sixteen students voted for cheese pizza. How many students voted for pepperoni pizza?

4 Chaz was elected president of the Wildlife Preservation Club. He got 56 times more votes than his opponent. If his opponent got 368 votes, how many votes did Chaz get?

5 Brooke's fourth-grade class voted on their favorite book. *Harriet, the Spy* got 28 times more votes than *The Boxcar Children*. If *The Boxcar Children* got 42 votes, how many votes did *Harriet, the Spy* get?

6 Forty-five times as many people voted in the 2001 election as in the 1999 election. If 489 people voted in the 1999 election, how many people voted in the 2001 election?

If I am elected president, I promise to outlaw peas!

7 Lewiston's governor received 76 times as many votes as Georgetown's governor. Georgetown's governor received 790 votes. How many votes did Lewiston's governor receive?

Did you know?
Three U.S. presidents died on July 4: John Adams, Thomas Jefferson and James Monroe.

Name _____ Date _____

◇ Start Here!

Solve each problem. The first problem is worked for you.

1 Jeremy is building a dog pen. Two of the sides are 17 feet long, and the other two sides are 21 feet long. How much fencing will Jeremy need?

Remember...
The perimeter is the distance around a figure. To find the perimeter of a figure, add up the lengths of each side of the figure.

$$
\begin{array}{r}
17 \\
21 \\
17 \\
+ 21 \\
\hline
76 \quad \text{feet of fencing}
\end{array}
$$

2 Heather is putting tile around the edge of her swimming pool. Her swimming pool measures 20 feet by 16 feet. How many feet of tile will Heather have to put down?

3 Beth needs enough ribbon to go around the perimeter of her blanket. If the blanket measures 45 inches by 60 inches, how many inches of ribbon will Beth need to buy?

4 Kim is fencing an area in her yard. If two of the edges are 45 feet, and the other two edges are 57 feet, how many feet of fencing will Kim need?

5 Max is making a frame for a picture he painted. The picture is 36 inches by 18 inches. How many inches will his finished frame be?

6 Lizzy is making a garden in her yard. What is the perimeter of her garden if each edge measures 36 feet?

7 Nancy is sewing trim around a tablecloth. If the tablecloth is 108 inches long and 72 inches wide, how many inches of trim does Nancy need?

Did you know?
U.S. currency measures 2.61 inches wide by 6.14 inches long and is .0043 inches thick. If the bills printed each year were laid end to end, they would stretch around the earth's equator approximately 24 times. Larger-sized notes in circulation before 1929 measured 3.125 inches by 7.4218 inches.

Amazing Area

Name _____   Date _____

◇ Start Here!

Rosa and her friends are building a clubhouse. Help her solve the problems.

Remember...
To find the area of a rectangular figure, multiply the length by the width.

1 ⟩ Rosa and Matt need to figure the area of the floor so they know how many boards to buy. If the floor is 8 feet by 12 feet, what is the area of the floor?

$$\begin{array}{r} 12 \\ \times\ 8 \\ \hline 96 \end{array}\ \text{square feet}$$

2 ⟩ Amy measures the area for the window. The window measures 16 inches wide and 21 inches tall. What is the area of the window?

3 ⟩ Dylan wants to paint the back door to the clubhouse. The door is 56 inches tall and 32 inches wide. What is the area of the door?

4 ⟩ Matt and Haley are working on the roof. They need to figure out the area so they will know how many supplies to buy. The roof is 108 inches by 156 inches. What is the area of the clubhouse roof?

5 ⟩ Ashley wants to carpet a space in the clubhouse that is 32 inches by 59 inches. What is the area of the space she wants to carpet?

6 ⟩ Rosa makes a small flower garden outside the clubhouse. The garden is 23 meters wide and 37 meters long. What is the area of Rosa's garden?

7 ⟩ Dylan plants grass in an area behind the clubhouse that is 14 feet wide and 54 feet long? What is the area that Dylan plants?

Name _____ Date _____

◇ Start Here!

Solve each problem. The first problem is worked for you.

1 The fourth grade is going on a field trip to the zoo. There are 108 students and 3 buses. How many students are on each bus?

$$108 \div 3 = 36 \text{ students}$$

2 The class visits the reptile house at the zoo. There are 245 reptiles. Each cage holds 5 reptiles. How many cages are there?

3 Robin's class takes a field trip to the museum. Robin sees 116 exhibits total. Each room has 4 exhibits in it. How many rooms does Robin go through?

4 Adrian's class is going to the theater. Half of the group goes into theater A. The other half of the group goes into theater B. If there are 114 students, how many students are in each theater?

5 Dan's class visits the natural history museum. The class sees 222 relics. If there are 6 relics in each room, how many rooms does the museum have?

6 Heather's class goes to a farm. At the farm, the class goes for a wagon ride. There are 105 students. If the wagon holds 7 students, how many trips will the wagon need to make so everyone gets a ride?

7 At the history museum, Danny's class breaks up into groups of 8 to look at the exhibits. If there are 168 students, how many groups are there?

8 There are 416 students who go to the movie theater. Each row seats 8 people. How many rows does the theater need to seat everyone?

Did you know?
Star Wars: Episode I—The Phantom Menace earned 431 million dollars in ticket sales. *Toy Story 2* earned 245.9 million dollars, and *The Lion King* earned 312.9 million dollars in ticket sales.

Name _____ Date _____

◇Start Here!
Solve each problem. The first problem is worked for you.

1 Pam's favorite flowers are daisies. Pam spends $7.88 on daisies. If Pam buys 4 bunches, how much does each bunch cost?

$$7.88 \div 4 = \$1.97$$

2 Todd buys 7 long-stem roses. Todd spends $6.51 on the roses. How much does each rose cost?

3 Jada wants some purple flowers. She buys a 6-pack of petunias for $4.32. How much does each petunia plant cost?

4 The plant nursery has a sale on geraniums. Lance buys a case with 9 geraniums for $12.51. How much does each geranium cost?

5 Marie buys an 8-pound bag of plant fertilizer for $19.92. What is the cost per pound for the plant fertilizer?

6 Penny wants some marigold plants. She spends $18.41 on 7 potted marigolds. How much does each potted marigold cost?

7 Eric needs a big bag of dirt. He finds a 5-pound bag of dirt on sale for $7.80. What is the cost per pound for the bag of dirt?

I'm growing a row of numbers.

8 Brittany likes tall plants. She buys a 4-pack of sunflower plants for $3.04. How much does Brittany spend for each sunflower plant?

Name _____ Date _____

◇ Start Here!

Solve each problem. The first problem is worked for you.

1. Marcy buys rulers for her class. Each box has 8 rulers. How many boxes does Marcy need if there are 85 students in her class?

$$85 \div 8 = 10 + \text{remainder of } 5$$
11 boxes

2. Craig has $37. He buys bottles of glue for $2 each. How many bottles of glue can Craig buy?

3. Justin buys notebooks for all 159 students in his class. If each carton contains 7 notebooks, how many cartons does Justin need to buy to give one notebook to each student?

4. Penny brings candy for the class. Each package of candy has 9 pieces. There are 67 students in her class. How many packages of candy does Penny need to bring?

5. Sam, shares stickers with his class. There are 5 stickers on a sheet. If there are 32 people in Sam's class, how many sheets of stickers does Sam need?

6. Chloe has $15 to spend on pencils. Each box of pencils costs $2. How many boxes of pencils can Chloe buy? How much money does Chloe have left after she buys the pencils?

7. There are 149 people in Ross's class. Ross buys erasers for each of the students. Erasers are sold 4 to a package. How many packages of erasers does Ross need to buy?

8. Janice has $269 to spend on books. Each book costs $8. How many books can Janice buy?

Did you know?
The Bureau of Engraving and Printing produces 37 million bills a day with a face value of approximately $696 million. Forty-five percent of the notes printed are $1 bills.

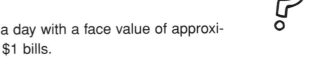

Name _____ Date _____

◇ Start Here!

Solve each problem. The first problem is worked for you.

1 The hotel has 243 rooms. If there are 27 rooms on each floor, how many floors are in the hotel?

243 ÷ 27 = 9 floors

2 James and his friends are at the Rent-a-Car lot. There are 392 cars. Each row has 56 cars. How many rows of cars are there on the lot?

3 Kim flies to California. On her flight, there are 144 passengers and 48 rows of seats. How many seats are in each row?

4 Lucy and her friends eat lunch at an Italian restaurant. The restaurant can seat 190 people. If there are 38 tables, how many people does each table seat?

5 Abby and her friends are visiting an amusement park. Their favorite ride, the Tidal Wave, holds 74 people. If two people fit in a car, how many cars are there on the ride?

6 Jan buys 66 postcards to send to her friends. If she sends postcards to 33 friends, how many postcards will each friend get?

Say, "Math vacation!"

7 Thomas and his friends go to a football game. There are 774 fans at the game. If there are 86 rows of seats, how many seats are in each row?

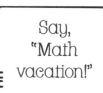

8 Max is waiting for his tour bus. Each bus can carry 47 tourists. If there are 282 tourists, how many tour buses are there?

Name _____ Date _____

◇ Start Here!

Solve each problem. The first problem is worked for you.

Remember...
- If you change a larger unit to a smaller unit (yards to feet), you multiply.
- If you change a smaller unit to a larger unit (inches to feet), you divide.

  12 inches = 1 foot
  3 feet = 1 yard
  36 inches = 1 yard

1 Pam needs 36 inches of rope. How many yards does she need to buy?

36 ÷ 12 = 3 feet = 1 yard

2 Jason needs 180 inches of string for his project. How many yards should he buy?

3 Maggie is carpeting her hall. The length of the hall is 14 feet. Carpet is sold by the yard. How many yards does Maggie need to buy so she will have enough?

4 Kristen is going to put together a puzzle that is 72 inches wide. Her table is 5 feet wide. How many inches wide is Kristen's table? Will her puzzle fit on the table?

5 The toy racetrack is 60 inches long. How many feet is the toy racetrack?

6 Andrea buys 7 yards of fabric. How many feet of fabric does she have?

7 Stuart is 5 feet and 9 inches tall. How many inches tall is Stuart?

8 Mike's garage is 22 feet long. His car is 108 inches long and his trailer is 140 inches long. How long is Mike's car and trailer altogether? Will both the car and trailer fit in the garage?

Kitchen Conversions

Name _____ Date _____

◇ Start Here!

Solve each problem. The first problem is worked for you.

Remember...
- If you change a larger unit to a smaller unit (tablespoon to teaspoon) you multiply.
- If you change a smaller unit to a larger unit (quart to gallon) you divide.

> 1 tablespoon = 3 teaspoons
> 1 pint = 2 cups
> 1 quart = 2 pints
> 1 gallon = 4 quarts
> 1 pound = 16 ounces

1 Maria's jam recipe calls for 8 pints of chopped fruit. How many quarts of chopped fruit does she need?

$$8 \div 2 = 4 \text{ quarts}$$

2 Ben needs 16 quarts of punch for the party. How many gallons of punch does Ben need to buy?

3 James is making cookies for a bake sale at his school. He uses 64 ounces of chocolate chips in his recipe. How many pounds of chocolate chips does use?

4 Mario needs 3 gallons of soup for his party. The restaurant packages his soup in quart bottles. How many bottles does he have to pick up?

5 Angela is making a triple-layer chocolate cake, and her recipe calls for 2 tablespoons of vanilla. Angela only has a teaspoon to measure with. How many teaspoons should she use?

6 Dennis is making salsa for his friends. He has 32 cups of salsa and puts it in 1-pint jars. How many 1-pint jars does Dennis need?

Name _____   Date _____

◇ Start Here!
Answer each question using the graph.

1   What is being compared on this graph?

dogs and cats adopted

2   How many cats were adopted in April?

3   How many dogs were adopted in June?

4   In which month were the most cats adopted?

5   How many more dogs than cats were adopted in May?

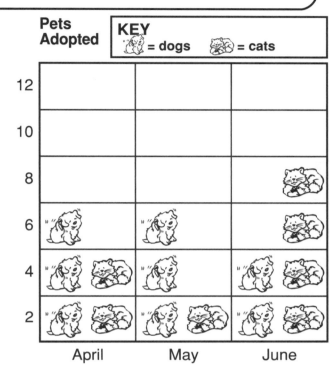

Pets Adopted

KEY   = dogs   = cats

---

1   What is being compared on this graph?

2   How many gerbils did the pet store sell on Tuesday?

3   Which day of the week were the most gerbils sold?

4   What was the total number of gerbils and guinea pigs sold on Wednesday?

5   Which day of the week did the pet store sell 8 guinea pigs?

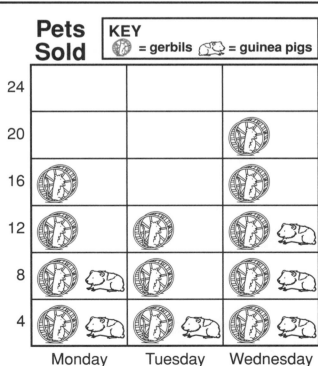

Pets Sold

KEY   = gerbils   = guinea pigs

Name _____ Date _____

◇Start Here!

Solve each problem. The first problem is worked for you.

1 Duane watches a car race. The red race car drives 7 1/10 miles. The silver race car drives 9 6/10 miles. How many miles more does the silver race car drive than the red race car?

Remember…
When the denominators are the same, subtract the numerators then the whole numbers.

$$9\frac{6}{10}$$
$$-7\frac{1}{10}$$
$$\overline{2\frac{5}{10}\text{ miles}}$$

2 The brown horse runs 3/12 of a mile farther than the black horse. The black horse runs 15 4/12 of a mile. How far does the brown horse run?

3 Karla runs 6 5/16 miles, and Jason runs 11 4/16 miles. How many miles do Karla and Jason run altogether?

4 Toby competes in a bicycle race. On the first day of the race he rides 17 4/23 miles. On the second day of the race he rides 22 12/23 miles. How far does Toby ride total?

5 John runs 10 3/6 meters. Erica runs 11 5/6 meters. How much farther does Erica run than John?

6 Mindy drives her car 35 6/12 times around the racetrack. Shannon drives her car 21 4/12 times around the racetrack. How many more times does Mindy drive her car around the racetrack than Shannon?

7 Jay swims 3/10 of a mile farther than Randy. If Randy swims 2 4/10 miles, how far does Jay swim?

8 Mario wins the race by 2/12 of a second. If his closest competitor's time was 11/12 of a second, what was Mario's time?

Did you know?
The average speed of a car driving in the Indianapolis 500 race in 2001 was 131.294 miles per hour.

Name _____ Date _____

◇ Start Here!

Ryan is making a birthday cake for his friend's birthday. Help him solve each problem.

1 Ryan needs 6 3/4 cups of flour for his recipe. When he measures the flour in his bag, he only has 3 2/3 cups of flour. How much more flour does Ryan need for his recipe?

$$6\frac{3}{4} = \qquad 6\frac{9}{12}$$
$$-3\frac{2}{3} = \qquad -3\frac{8}{12}$$
$$\overline{\quad 3\frac{1}{12} \text{ cups of flour}}$$

Remember...
When adding or subtracting fractions with different denominators, first find the lowest common denominator for the fractions. Convert the fractions, then add or subtract the numerators.

2 Next, the recipe says to sift together 5/8 teaspoon of baking power with 1/3 teaspoon of salt. How many teaspoons does Ryan sift altogether?

3 Ryan adds 1 2/3 cups of sugar and realizes he put in too much sugar. He takes out 1/4 cup of sugar from the mixing bowl. How much sugar did Ryan use in the recipe?

4 Applesauce is the next ingredient Ryan needs to add. He measures 5/8 cup and then adds 1/9 cup. How much applesauce did Ryan add altogether?

5 Ryan has a full carton of 12 eggs. He uses 1/3 of the carton. How many eggs does Ryan have left?

6 Ryan bakes the cake for 25 5/12 minutes. He decides it needs to bake longer. He bakes it for another 2 3/6 minutes. How long does the cake bake altogether?

7 Next, Ryan frosts the birthday cake. He uses 1 5/6 cups of frosting and then adds another 3/8 cup of frosting. How much frosting does Ryan use altogether?

8 Last, Ryan puts the candles on the cake. Ryan has a full box of 12 candles. He uses 5/6 of the box. How many candles does Ryan have left?

Name _____ Date _____

◇**Start Here!**

Solve each problem. The first problem is worked for you.

1 Henry runs three and six-tenths miles. Write the decimal number that shows how many miles Henry runs.

3.6

2 Dotty scores twenty-three and two-tenths points. Write the decimal number that shows how many points Dotty scores.

3 Jacob's kite flies sixty-nine and five-hundredths yards. Write the decimal number that shows how many yards Jacob's kite flies.

4 Becky swims two and thirty-five-hundredths miles. Write the decimal number that shows how many miles Becky swims.

5 Max scored twenty-eight and two-tenths points. Write the decimal number that shows how many points Max scored.

6 Jackson drives fifty-eight and forty-five-hundredths miles. Write the decimal number that shows how many miles Jackson drives.

7 Brad throws the ball twenty-one and three-tenths feet. Write the decimal number that shows how many feet Brad throws the ball.

8 Claire jogs six and nine-tenths miles. Write the decimal number that shows how many miles Claire jogs.

9 Mitch earns ten and forty-five-thousandths points. Write the decimal number that shows how many points Mitch earns.

Name _____ Date _____

◇ Start Here!

Solve each problem. The first problem is worked for you.

Remember...

To add and subtract decimals, you must first line up the decimal points. Put in zeros for any missing numbers. Add or subtract. Remember to put the decimal point in the answer.

 1 Eve drives 67.4 miles farther than Tyler. If Tyler drives 45.39 miles, how many miles does Eve drive?

$$
\begin{array}{r}
67.40 \\
+\ 45.39 \\
\hline
112.79 \quad \text{miles}
\end{array}
$$

2 In 2000, 47.8 percent of the cars sold in the U.S. were midsize cars. The percentage of small cars sold was 28.1 percent. How many more midsize cars were sold than small cars?

3 Brett drives 95.3 miles on Friday and 76.9 miles on Saturday. How many miles did Brett drive altogether?

4 In 1999, 16.5 percent of people in the U.S. bought luxury cars. That same year, 52.7 percent of the people in the U.S. bought midsize cars. What was the total percentage of people that bought either luxury cars or midsize cars?

 5 Dean's truck gets 15.3 miles per gallon of gas. Christy's car gets 25.2 miles per gallon of gas. How many more miles per gallon does Christy's car get than Dean's truck?

 6 Silver was the most popular color of sports car sold in the U.S. in 2000. In that year, 22.3 percent of the sports cars sold were silver, and 14.4 percent of the sports cars sold were black. How many more silver sports cars were sold than black cars?

Name _____ Date _____

◇ Start Here!

Solve each problem. The first problem is worked for you.

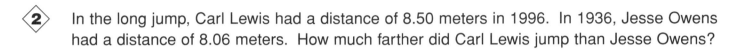

1 In 1996, the best time for the 400-meter hurdles was 47.54 seconds. The best time in 1980 was 48.70 seconds. How much faster was the time in 1996 than the time in 1980?

$$
\begin{array}{r}
48.70 \\
- 47.54 \\
\hline
1.16 \ \text{seconds}
\end{array}
$$

---

2 In the long jump, Carl Lewis had a distance of 8.50 meters in 1996. In 1936, Jesse Owens had a distance of 8.06 meters. How much farther did Carl Lewis jump than Jesse Owens?

3 U.S. speed skater Bonnie Blair won the Olympic gold medal for women's 500-meter speed skating in 1992 and 1994. In 1992, her time was 40.33 seconds. In 1994, her time was 39.25 seconds. How much faster was Bonnie's time in 1994 than her time in 1992?

4 In 2000, the 100-meter freestyle was completed in 48.30 seconds. In 1972, the 100-meter freestyle was completed in 51.22 seconds. How many seconds more did it take to complete the 100-meter freestyle in 1972?

5 The U.S. won gold medals in the women's 100-meter run in both 1996 and 2000. The winning time in 1996 was 10.94 seconds. The winning time in 2000 was 10.75 seconds. How much faster was the winning time in 2000 than in 1996?

> Use math to get the gold!

6 In 1994, Jean-Luc Brassard won the gold medal in men's moguls freestyle skiing with 27.24 points. In 1998, Jonny Moseley won the gold medal with 26.93 points. How many more points did Brassard have than Moseley?

Did you know?

The symbol for the Olympic Games is five rings. Each ring symbolizes a continent: Europe, Asia, Africa, Australia and America. The blue, yellow, black, green and red rings are linked together to represent the friendship of all people.

Answer Pages

Page 3
1. 41 grasshoppers and beetles
2. 53 black ants
3. 59 caterpillars
4. 61 spiders
5. 43 ladybugs
6. 37 bees
7. 40 butterflies

Page 4
1. 831 pounds of food
2. 97 reptiles
3. 6,891 people
4. 111 pictures
5. 6,250 ounces of birdseed
6. 150 cages
7. 419 feet
8. 245 animals

Page 5
1. 46 feet
2. 323 feet
3. 73 feet
4. 204 feet
5. 9,490 feet
6. 8,715 feet
7. 83 feet

Page 6
1. 1,358 tropical fish
2. 7,628 feet
3. 5,425 seashells
4. 2,326 feet
5. 127 sea urchins
6. 523 sea creatures
7. 1,984 fish
8. 1,877 feet

Page 7
1. $86.30
2. $52.69
3. $43.37
4. $133.20
5. $15.29
6. $16.33
7. $97.85
8. $15.36

Page 8
1. 494 calories
2. 44 calories
3. 378 calories
4. pizza
5. 321 calories
6. 495 calories
7. celery

Page 9
1. 40
2. 40
3. 20
4. 400
5. 700
6. 400
7. 5,000
8. 2,000

Page 10
1. 144 ounces
2. 972¢ or $9.72
3. 147 glasses
4. 49 pitchers
5. 243¢ or $2.43
6. 7 cups
7. 9,758¢ or $97.58
8. $164.43
9. 16 glasses

Page 11
1. 24
2. 85
3. 85
4. 82

Page 12
1. 2 gallons
2. May
3. March
4. January
5. 10 gallons

1. vanilla
2. 18%
3. rocky road
4. 48%

Page 13
1. 116 tennis rackets
2. 136 footballs
3. 160 snowboards
4. 104 dumbbells
5. 168 skates
6. 456 skateboards
7. 108 helmets
8. 84 baseballs

Page 14
1. 12,951 magazines
2. 2,990 words
3. 278 pictures
4. 20,696 magazines
5. 2,394 magazines
6. 1,036 pages
7. 34,578 subscriptions

Page 15
1. $8.68
2. $46.80
3. $148.32
4. $148.98
5. $22.77
6. $408.73
7. $55.08
8. $167.86

Page 16
1. 2,890 votes
2. 837 students
3. 208 students
4. 20,608 votes
5. 1,176 votes
6. 22,005 votes
7. 60,040 votes

Page 17
1. 76 feet
2. 72 feet
3. 210 inches
4. 204 feet
5. 108 inches
6. 144 feet
7. 360 inches

www.rbpbooks.com reproducible **MBS—Math Word Problems Grade 4**

Page 18
1. 96 square feet
2. 336 square inches
3. 1,792 square inches
4. 16,848 square inches
5. 1,888 square inches
6. 851 square meters
7. 756 square feet

Page 19
1. 36 students
2. 49 cages
3. 29 rooms
4. 57 students
5. 37 rooms
6. 15 trips
7. 21 groups
8. 52 rows

Page 20
1. $1.97
2. $.93
3. $.72
4. $1.39
5. $2.49
6. $2.63
7. $1.56
8. $.76

Page 21
1. 11 boxes
2. 18 bottles
3. 23 cartons
4. 8 packages
5. 7 sheets
6. 7 boxes with $1.00 left over
7. 38 packages
8. 33 books

Page 22
1. 9 floors
2. 7 rows
3. 3 seats
4. 5 people
5. 37 cars
6. 2 postcards
7. 9 seats
8. 6 buses

Page 23
1. 1 yard
2. 5 yards
3. 5 yards
4. 60 inches, no
5. 5 feet
6. 21 feet
7. 69 inches
8. 248 inches, yes

Page 24
1. 4 quarts
2. 4 gallons
3. 4 pounds
4. 12 bottles
5. 6 teaspoons
6. 16 jars

Page 25
1. dogs and cats adopted
2. 4 cats
3. 4 dogs
4. June
5. 4 dogs

1. gerbils and guinea pigs sold
2. 12 gerbils
3. Wednesday
4. 32 gerbils and guinea pigs
5. Monday

Page 26
1. 2 5/10 miles
2. 15 7/12 miles
3. 17 9/16 miles
4. 39 16/23 miles
5. 1 2/6 meters
6. 14 2/12 times
7. 2 7/10 miles
8. 9/12 second

Page 27
1. 3 1/12 cups flour
2. 23/24 teaspoon
3. 17/12 or 1 5/12 cup
4. 53/72 cup
5. 8/12, 8 eggs or 2/3 of a carton
6. 27 11/12 minutes
7. 53/24 or 2 5/24 cups
8. 2/12, 2 candles or 1/6 of the box

Page 28
1. 3.6
2. 23.2
3. 69.05
4. 2.35
5. 28.2
6. 58.45
7. 21.3
8. 6.9
9. 10.045

Page 29
1. 112.79 miles
2. 19.7 percent
3. 172.2 miles
4. 69.2 percent
5. 9.9 miles per gallon
6. 7.9 percent

Page 30
1. 1.16 seconds
2. .44 meters
3. 1.08 seconds
4. 2.92 seconds
5. .19 seconds
6. .31 points

Rainbow Bridge Publishing
Certificate
of Completion

Awarded to

_____

for the completion of
Mastering Basic Skills

George Starr

_____   _____
Publisher's Signature   Parent's Signature

Receive RBP's FREE Parent and Teacher on-line newsletter!

Receive special offers, FREE learning exercises and great ideas to use in your classroom and at home!

To receive our on-line newsletter, please provide us with the following information:

Name:_____

Address:_____

City:_____ State: ____ Zip: _____

Email Address:_____

Store where book was purchased: _____

Child's grade level: _____

Book title purchased:_____

Or visit our website:

www.sbakids.com

Or Call:
801-268-8887

Summer Bridge Activities™

Title	Price
Grade P-K	$12.95
Grade K-1	$12.95
Grade 1-2	$12.95
Grade 2-3	$12.95
Grade 3-4	$12.95
Grade 4-5	$12.95
Grade 5-6	$12.95

Summer Bridge Middle School™

Title	Price
Grade 6-7	$12.95
Grade 7-8	$12.95

Summer Bridge Reading Activities™

Title	Price
Grade 1-2	$6.95
Grade 2-3	$6.95
Grade 3-4	$6.95

Summer Journal™

Title	Price
Summer Journal™	$4.95

Summer Dailies™

Title	Price
Summer Dailies™	$4.95

Summer Traveler™

Title	Price
Summer Traveler™	$4.95

Math Bridge™

Title	Price
Grade 1	$9.95
Grade 2	$9.95
Grade 3	$9.95
Grade 4	$9.95
Grade 5	$9.95
Grade 6	$9.95
Grade 7	$9.95
Grade 8	$9.95

Reading Bridge™

Title	Price
Grade 1	$9.95
Grade 2	$9.95
Grade 3	$9.95
Grade 4	$9.95
Grade 5	$9.95
Grade 6	$9.95
Grade 7	$9.95
Grade 8	$9.95

Skill Builders™

Title	Price
Phonics Grade 1	$2.50
Spelling Grade 2	$2.50
Vocabulary Grade 3	$2.50
Reading Grade 1	$2.50
Reading Grade 2	$2.50
Reading Grade 3	$2.50
Math Grade 1	$2.50
Math Grade 2	$2.50
Math Grade 3	$2.50
Subtraction Grade 1	$2.50
Subtraction Grade 2	$2.50
Multiplication Grade 3	$2.50

Connection Series™

Title	Price
Reading Grade 1	$10.95
Reading Grade 2	$10.95
Reading Grade 3	$10.95
Math Grade 1	$10.95
Math Grade 2	$10.95
Math Grade 3	$10.95

Mastering Basic Skills™

Title	Price
Grammar Grade 1	$5.95
Grammar Grade 2	$5.95
Grammar Grade 3	$5.95
Word Problems Grade 1	$4.95
Word Problems Grade 2	$4.95
Word Problems Grade 3	$4.95
Word Problems Grade 4	$4.95
Listening Skills Grade 1	$4.95
Listening Skills Grade 2	$4.95
Listening Skills Grade 3	$4.95

Math Test Preparation™

Title	Price
Math Test Prep Grade 1	$10.95
Math Test Prep Grade 2	$10.95
Math Test Prep Grade 3	$10.95

First Step Spanish™

Title	Price
Colors/Shapes	$5.95
Alphabet/Numbers	$5.95

Place Proper Postage Here

**Rainbow Bridge Publishing
PO Box 571470
Salt Lake City, Utah 84157**

Keeping Children Busy, Happy, and Learning During the Summer and Beyond!